Discover & Learn

Living Planet

This Activity Book is packed with questions
to help KS2 pupils explore life on planet Earth,
including physical and human aspects.

Please note:

Pupils will need the matching CGP 'Living Planet'
Study Book to answer the questions in this Activity Book.

Published by CGP

Consultant: Joanna Copley

Author: Mark McDermott

Editors: Mary Falkner, Sarah Pattison, Rebecca Russell, Caroline Thomson

ISBN: 978 1 78294 985 5

With thanks to Ellen Burton and Emma Espley for the proofreading.

With thanks to Jan Greenway for the copyright research.

Printed by Elanders Ltd, Newcastle upon Tyne

Clipart from Corel®

Contents

Section One – Life on Earth

The Solar System

Read pages 2 and 3 of the Study Book about the planets of the Solar System, then answer these questions.

1. Look at this diagram of the Solar System. Circle the Earth.

You can use a funny sentence to help you remember the order of the planets.

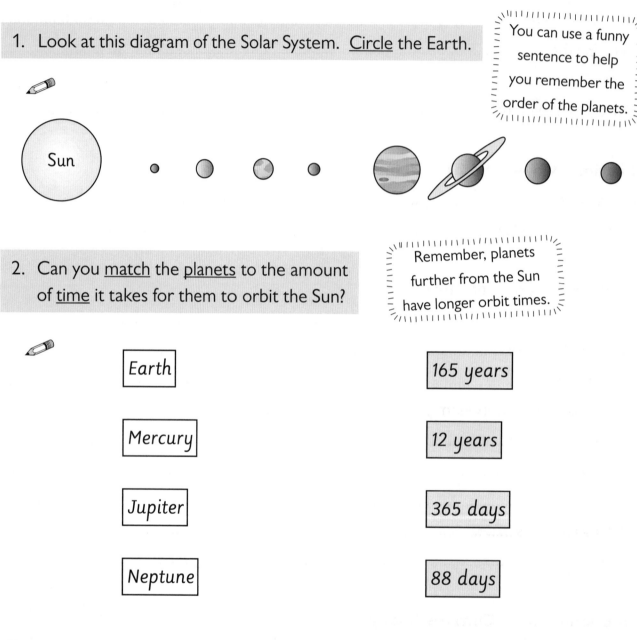

2. Can you match the planets to the amount of time it takes for them to orbit the Sun?

Remember, planets further from the Sun have longer orbit times.

Earth		165 years
Mercury		12 years
Jupiter		365 days
Neptune		88 days

3. Can you explain in your own words what is meant by 'The Goldilocks Zone'?

The Goldilocks Zone is ....

....

....

....

4. Read each statement below and decide
   if it is <u>true</u> or <u>false</u>. <u>Tick</u> the correct box.

Saturn is made completely of gases.   True ☐ False ☐

The Earth spins at 600 miles per hour.   True ☐ False ☐

Mars is the closest planet to the Sun.   True ☐ False ☐

The atmosphere of Earth is mainly made up
of nitrogen and oxygen.   True ☐ False ☐

5. Read the <u>clues</u> to complete this crossword.

<u>Across</u>

1 A planet that has large rings.

3 How many planets there are in
   the Solar System.

7 A type of large planet that's
   made mostly of gases.

8 The planet closest to the Sun.

<u>Down</u>

2 The planet furthest from the Sun.

4 The path a planet takes
   around the Sun.

5 The seventh planet from the Sun.

6 How many years it takes for the
   Earth to orbit the Sun.

"I know about the Solar System and the planets in it.
I know how the Earth moves around the Sun."

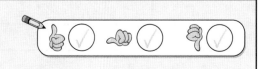

Why Earth?

Read pages 4 and 5 of the Study Book to help you answer these questions.

1. What are the four main 'ingredients' that support life on Earth?

    1) ....

    2) ....

    3) ....

    4) ....

2. Imagine you could fit all the land and all the water on Earth into one big box. Use two different coloured pencils to colour in how much of the box would be full of land and how much would be full of water.

Take a look back at page 4 of the Study Book to remind yourself about how much of the Earth's surface is covered by land.

KEY

☐ ....

☐ ....

3. Using the information in the Study Book and thinking about what you have learned already, explain, in your own words, why life doesn't exist on any other planets in our Solar System.

4. Give three reasons why the Earth's atmosphere is so important.

1) ....

2) ....

3) ....

5. Why is sunlight so important for life on Earth?

Sunlight is so important for life on Earth because ....

....

....

....

"I understand why Earth can support life."

What Time Is It?

Pages 6 and 7 of the Study Book are about the world's time zones and why they're important. Read both pages then answer the questions below.

1. Read page 6 of the Study Book. Use the words below to <u>complete</u> these sentences to <u>explain why</u> different places have different <u>time zones</u>.

midnight   time zones   12 pm   twenty-four   axis

The Earth spins on its .... once every

.... hours, so when it's midday on one side

of the Earth, it's .... on the other side.

We have different .... so that every country

can have midday at ....

2. Before standard time was agreed, people used the position of the <u>Sun</u> to tell the <u>time</u>. Why could this be a <u>problem</u> for people living in <u>different parts</u> of the UK?

This could be a problem for people living in different parts of the UK

because ....

....

....

....

....

....

3. If it's 12 pm in <u>London</u> what time is it in these cities?

Istanbul ....

Tokyo ....

New York ....

You can use the time zone map on page 7 of the Study Book for help. You can also use an atlas to help you find out which countries these cities are in if you're not sure.

4. Noa is flying from London in the UK to Miami in Florida. Her flight takes off at <u>2 pm</u> and takes <u>10 hours</u>. What time will it be <u>in Miami</u> when she lands?

Look at the time zone map on page 7 again for help.

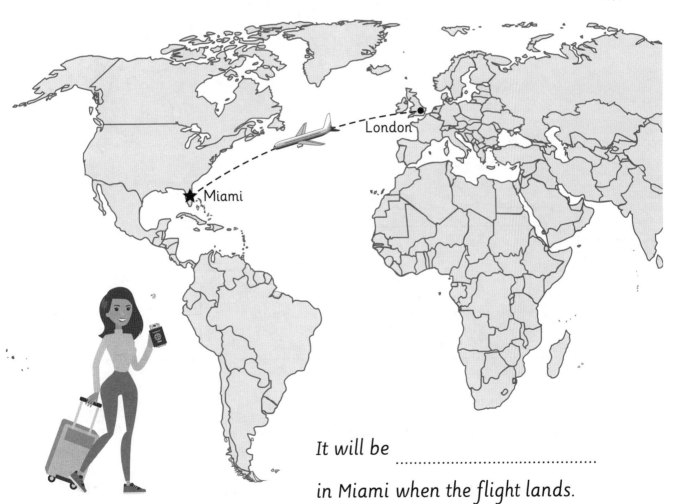

It will be ....

in Miami when the flight lands.

"I understand that it's not the same time all over the world and I know why we have time zones."

More Than Weather

Read pages 8 and 9 of the Study Book, then answer these questions about climate.

1. Look closely at the map on pages 8-9 of the Study Book.
    On the map below, carefully <u>colour</u> the <u>climate zones</u>
    and fill in the <u>key</u> to explain what each colour <u>means</u>.

You don't have to use the same colours as in the Study Book.

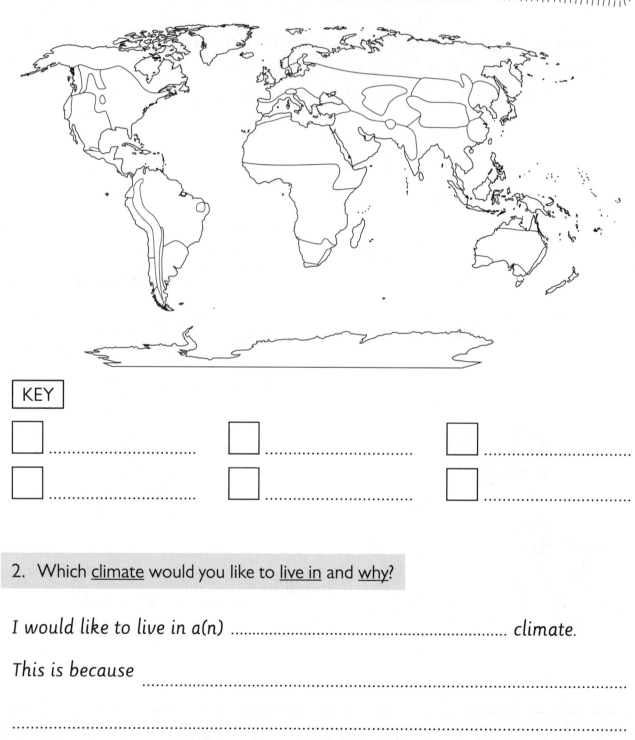

KEY

☐ ....   ☐ ....   ☐ ....

☐ ....   ☐ ....   ☐ ....

2. Which <u>climate</u> would you like to <u>live in</u> and <u>why</u>?

I would like to live in a(n) .... *climate.*

This is because ....

....

....

3. Imagine you're going to visit <u>Rome</u> in the summer. <u>Draw</u> the <u>clothes</u> you would take with you and <u>explain</u> why you would take them.

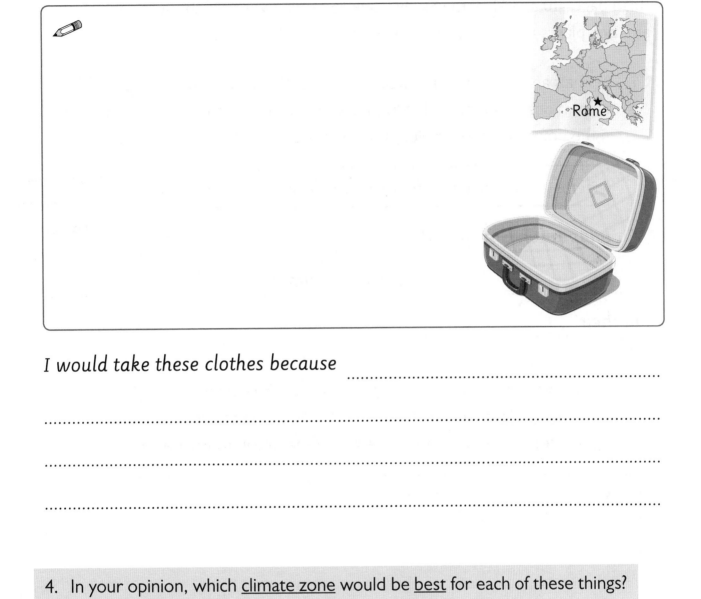

I would take these clothes because ....

....

....

....

4. In your opinion, which <u>climate zone</u> would be <u>best</u> for each of these things?

A nice, relaxing holiday ....

Growing wheat ....

Stopping food from going rotten ....

Being able to throw away your raincoat ....

"I can name the different climate zones of the world and explain what each one is like."

Section Two – The Blue Planet

Ocean Life

Read pages 10 and 11 of the Study Book to remind yourself about all the amazing plants and animals that you find living in the oceans.

1. Animals and plants that live near the <u>top</u> of the ocean have different <u>adaptations</u> to the ones that live near the <u>bottom</u> of the ocean. Use the words in the box below to <u>complete</u> this sentence to <u>explain</u> what an adaptation is.

    | helps   eat   survive   feature   environment   predator |

    You only need to use some of the words.

    An adaptation is a special .... *that*

    .... *a plant or animal* ....

    in their ....

2. <u>Imagine</u> you are a <u>diver</u> swimming down into the ocean. Write a <u>description</u> of your dive. Write about the things you might <u>see</u> and <u>feel</u> as you went from the top of the ocean to the deeper bits.

3. In which <u>part</u> of the ocean would you expect to find the <u>most</u>
    living things? <u>Tick</u> your answer, then <u>explain</u> the reasons for your choice.

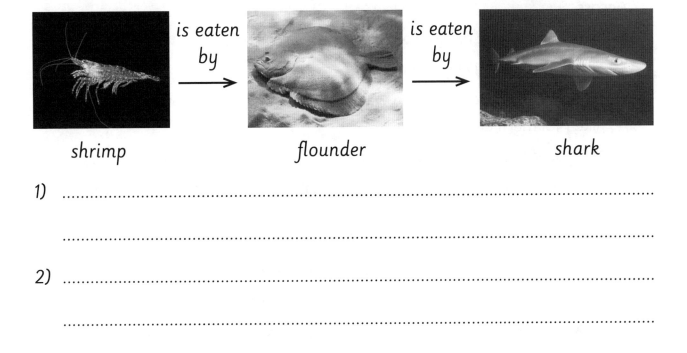

← ———— The sunlight zone ☐

← ———— The twilight zone ☐

← ———— The midnight zone ☐

I think this because ....

....

....

4. Look at the picture below. It shows part of an <u>ocean food chain</u>.
    The flounder has good <u>camouflage</u>, which makes it difficult for other
    animals to <u>see it</u>. Give <u>two reasons</u> why this is useful for the flounder.

is eaten by   →   *is eaten by*   →

shrimp   flounder   shark

1) ....

    ....

2) ....

    ....

"I know about the world's oceans and
understand that plants and animals that live
in the ocean are adapted to their environment."

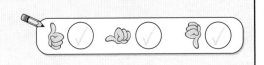

Oceans and the Climate

Pages 12 and 13 of the Study Book are all about how the oceans affect our climate. Make sure you've read those pages before answering these questions.

1. Read the clues and complete this crossword.

Across

2   The current that brings warm water towards the UK.

3   Tiny plants that live in the oceans.

7   Ocean currents carry warm water from _____ regions to colder places, like Northern Europe.

8   The oceans soak up heat from the _____ , which warms them up.

9   Lots of the plants from 3 Across can make the ocean look this colour.

Down

1   A gas that plants take in during photosynthesis.

4   A gas that plants give out during photosynthesis.

5   2 Across flows past the _____ coast of Canada.

6   Ocean currents are caused by _____ and by the rotation of the Earth.

2. Read these statements about ocean currents and decide whether each one is true or false. Tick the correct box for each one.

Ocean currents can be on the surface or underwater.   True ☐   False ☐

Ocean currents move warm water around the world.   True ☐   False ☐

The Gulf Stream passes the UK on its eastern side.   True ☐   False ☐

3. Design a leaflet to explain to people why phytoplankton are important to humans.

4. What do you think might happen to the UK if the Gulf Stream changed direction and no longer flowed towards the UK? Explain your answer.

....

....

....

"I know how phytoplankton and ocean currents can affect climate."

Section Three – Natural Earth

Mountains

Pages 14 and 15 of the Study Book are about mountain biomes and how we use them. Read the pages, then answer these questions.

1. What is a biome?

A biome is ....

....

....

2. More and more people are using mountains for leisure activities, like climbing and skiing. However, different people have different opinions about whether this is a good or bad thing. What might these people say about using the mountains for leisure? Fill in the speech bubbles.

tourist   environmentalist   skier   local resident

3. What <u>mountain range</u> is <u>Mount Everest</u> part of? <u>Circle</u> the correct answer.

The Alps   The Pennines   The Rocky Mountains

The Pyrenees   The Himalayas

4. List <u>three adaptations</u> that help the snow leopard survive in an alpine biome.

1) ....

2) ....

3) ....

5. Think about where you live. List ways that it is <u>similar</u> and ways that it is <u>different</u> to living in an <u>alpine environment</u> in the table below.

Similarities:	Differences:

"I know about alpine biomes, the plants and animals you can find there, and how humans use this biome."

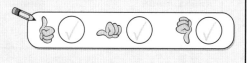

Tropical Rainforests

Take a look at pages 16 and 17 of the Study Book to help you answer these questions.

1. Fill in the <u>table</u> below with the names of each <u>layer</u> of the rainforest. Then read the <u>fact files</u> about the four rainforest animals and decide which one is found in each layer.

<u>Wild pig</u>

Eats grass and berries.

Sleeps in piles of leaves.

<u>Jaguar</u>

Jumps down on its prey from low branches.

Sharp claws for holding on to trees.

<u>Harpy eagle</u>

Likes to be out in the open.

Swoops down on its prey from above.

<u>Spider monkey</u>

Eats fruit and insects.

Very long arms to hold on to high branches.

	Name of layer	Animal that lives there
1		
2		
3		
4		

2. Paper is an example of a resource that we get from the rainforest.
Give one advantage and one disadvantage of taking this resource.

Advantage:

Disadvantage:

3. Imagine you and your family live in the rainforest. Describe some of
the problems you might face living there. Think about the climate, the
animals, where you would live and what your parents might do for work.

4. Explain in your own words what 'endangered'
means when talking about an animal.

Endangered means ....

....

"I know about tropical rainforest biomes, the plants and
animals found there, and how humans use this biome."

Woodlands

Turn to pages 18 and 19 of the Study Book to help you answer these questions about the different types of woodland around the world.

1. What is the <u>difference</u> between <u>coniferous</u> and <u>deciduous</u> trees?

Coniferous trees ....

....

Deciduous trees ....

....

2. Look at the map on page 18 of the Study Book. Can you explain <u>why</u> the coniferous and deciduous forests are <u>located</u> where they are?

3. <u>Chipmunks</u> live in burrows in the forest, and like to eat nuts, seeds and fruit. They have <u>sharp claws</u>. How do you think their sharp claws help them to <u>survive</u> in the forest?

I think sharp claws help chipmunks to survive in the forest because

....

....

4. How many <u>seasons</u> are there in a temperate climate?

There are .... *seasons in a temperate climate.*

5. Look at the statements in the boxes below about the effects of cutting down woodland. <u>Colour</u> the box <u>green</u> if you think it's a <u>good</u> thing, and <u>red</u> if you think it's a <u>bad</u> thing. Then decide if you think cutting down woodland is good or bad <u>overall</u>, and <u>explain</u> your answer.

Cutting down woodland...

...gives us wood for burning.	*...causes animals to lose their habitats.*
...gives people jobs and money.	*...gives us wood for paper.*

...can damage other plants and trees in the area.

...causes animals to lose their food sources.

I think cutting down woodland is good / bad overall. I think this

because ....

....

....

....

....

"I know about coniferous and deciduous woodlands and the plants and animals you can find there."

Hot, Cold and In-Between

Read pages 20 and 21 of the Study Book to help you answer these questions.

1. Colour in the <u>locations</u> of the different types of <u>desert</u> around the world.

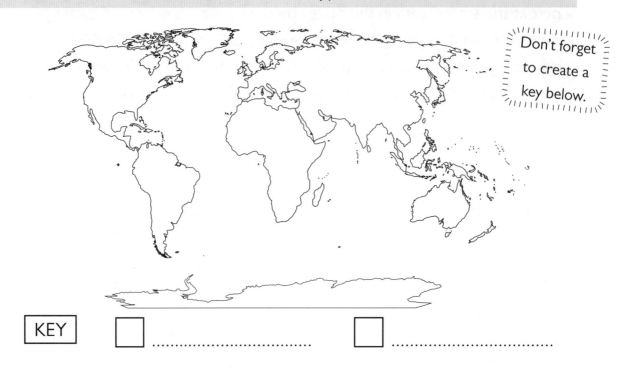

Don't forget to create a key below.

| KEY | ☐ .... | ☐ .... |

2. Read each statement below and decide if it is <u>true</u> or <u>false</u>. <u>Tick</u> the correct box.

All deserts are hot.   True ☐   False ☐

There are no hot deserts in Europe.   True ☐   False ☐

Most of Australia is covered by desert.   True ☐   False ☐

Not many plants live in the desert because the animals eat them all.   True ☐   False ☐

3. Give <u>two</u> reasons why tourists might prefer visiting the <u>Mediterranean</u> to visiting the <u>Arctic</u>.

1) ....

2) ....

4. Read the fact file about <u>jackrabbits</u>. Do you think they have adapted to living in a desert? <u>Explain</u> your answer.

<u>Jackrabbits</u>

- Nocturnal
- Large ears
- Grey and brown fur
- Fur-covered feet
- Fast runners
- Eat succulent plants, like cacti

I think / don't think they have adapted to live in the desert, because

....

....

....

5. <u>Forest fires</u> start easily in Mediterranean biomes. Design a poster to encourage people to think about forest fires. What might <u>cause</u> the fire? What could people do to lessen the <u>risk</u> of causing a fire?

"I know about hot and cold desert biomes and Mediterranean biomes."

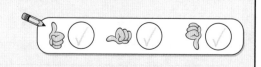

Grasslands

Turn to pages 22 and 23 of the Study Book to help you with these questions.

1. What is a savannah?

A savannah is ....

....

2. Draw one of the animals from page 23 of the Study Book and label the features that make it well adapted to its environment.

3. List three similarities and three differences between a temperate grassland biome and a savannah biome.

Similarities:	Differences:

4. Sometimes, areas of savannah are turned into deserts because of human actions. Tick the things you think would make a savannah more like a desert.

| | Littering. | | Cutting down the plants and trees. |
| | Planting trees. | | Letting farm animals eat the vegetation. |

5. These graphs show the average temperature and rainfall in a savannah biome and a temperate grassland biome. Look at the graphs and decide which graphs represent which biome.

Look back at page 22 of the Study Book to remind yourself of the climate in each biome.

Biome 1

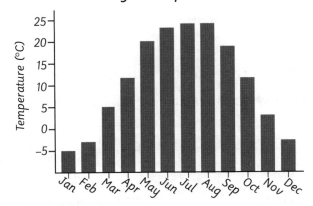

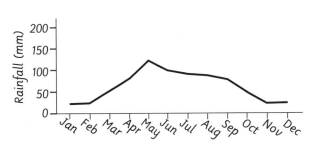

These graphs represent a .... biome.

Biome 2

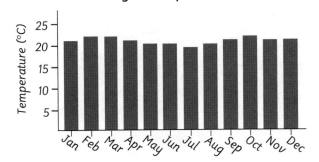

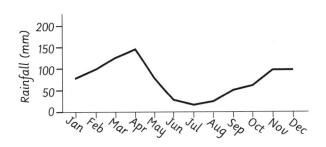

These graphs represent a .... biome.

"I know about temperate grasslands and savannahs, their climates and the plants and animals that live there."

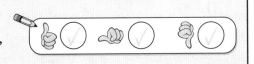

A Frozen Place

Read pages 24 and 25 of the Study Book to help you answer these questions.

1. What's the <u>difference</u> between <u>tundra biomes</u> and <u>polar deserts</u>?

2. Look at this picture of an <u>Arctic fox</u>. Identify <u>three</u> features that make it suited to living in the Arctic and <u>explain</u> how each feature helps it survive.

Hint: think about some of the adaptations mentioned on page 25 of the Study Book.

1) ....

....

2) ....

....

3) ....

....

3. Imagine you have been asked to design a new coat that is inspired by a <u>polar bear's fur</u>. Draw a <u>picture</u> of your coat and <u>label</u> the features that will help make it <u>warm</u> and <u>waterproof</u>.

> Use the information about polar bears on page 25 of the Study Book to give you some ideas.

4. Write down some reasons why crude oil pipelines are considered to be <u>good</u> and <u>bad</u>. Then decide if you think they should be <u>banned</u> from the tundra. <u>Explain</u> your answer.

Good:

Bad:

I think crude oil pipelines should / shouldn't be banned from the tundra,

because ....

....

....

"I know about tundra biomes, how people use them, and some of the plants and animals you can find there."

Water Worlds

Read pages 26 and 27 of the Study Book, then answer these questions.

1. What are the two main water biomes?

1) ....

2) ....

2. Why do you think the land that goes into the sea is called the continental shelf?

I think the land that goes into the sea is called the continental shelf

because ....

....

....

3. Read each statement below and decide if
   it is true or false. Tick the correct box.

Mangroves can grow in salt water.	True ☐	False ☐
The coastal biome can be found in the ocean, beyond the edge of the continental shelf.	True ☐	False ☐
A wetland biome is flat.	True ☐	False ☐
The Fens are in the west of England.	True ☐	False ☐
The coastal biome is rich in plant and animal life.	True ☐	False ☐
Bitterns pretend to be plants when they want to hide.	True ☐	False ☐

4. Draw pictures of a <u>salt water biome</u> and a <u>fresh water biome</u> in the boxes below. Draw some of the <u>creatures</u> that live in each one.

✎ Salt water biome	✎ Fresh water biome

5. In the 1600s, the Fens were drained to make more <u>farmland</u>. In 2003, some of these areas were <u>re-flooded</u>. This meant that some plants and animals that had disappeared could <u>return</u> to the area. Do you think this was a <u>good</u> idea? If you were in charge, would you keep the land as <u>farmland</u> or return it to its <u>natural state</u>? <u>Explain</u> your answer.

Do you think it was a good idea to re-flood the Fens?   Yes ☐ No ☐

If I were in charge, I would ....

....

I would do this because ....

....

....

....

"I know about salt water and fresh water biomes and the plants and animals that you can find there." 👍✓ 🤙✓ 👎✓

Making Changes

Use pages 28 and 29 of the Study Book to help you answer these questions.

1. Read the <u>magazine article</u> below about food miles. Do you think we should only eat food that's grown <u>locally</u>, or should we continue to <u>import</u> foods from other countries? <u>Explain</u> your answer.

I think we should ....

....

....

because ....

....

....

....

....

....

....

What are food miles?

Food miles are the <u>distance</u> that food has travelled from where it was <u>grown</u> to where it is <u>eaten</u>. Over <u>half</u> of the food in UK supermarkets is <u>imported</u> from other countries. Many fruits and vegetables are grown in <u>hot</u> countries such as Ghana and Costa Rica. These foods have <u>high</u> food miles because they come from <u>far away</u>, usually by <u>aeroplane</u>. The planes give out <u>gases</u> that are <u>harmful</u> to the environment. Some people say we should only buy foods with <u>low</u> food miles to <u>reduce</u> these harmful gases. This is food that's grown <u>locally</u> and doesn't have to travel <u>far</u>. But buying foods from <u>abroad</u> can help people in other countries to earn <u>money</u>. It also means we can get many <u>different</u> <u>types</u> of food that can't be grown in the UK.

2. Why was <u>water pollution</u> not so much of a problem when the Ancient Egyptians first settled along the banks of the Nile around <u>7000 years ago</u>?

Water pollution wasn't so much of a problem when the Ancient Egyptians

first settled along the banks of the Nile, because ....

....

....

3. Using <u>less plastic</u> and <u>recycling</u> old plastic can help to <u>reduce</u> the amount of plastic waste that ends up in the oceans and in landfills. Design an <u>advert</u> for a school newsletter to encourage people to <u>reduce</u> the amount of <u>plastic</u> they throw away.

4. Plastics are very <u>useful</u>, but they can be <u>harmful</u> to humans and wildlife. <u>List</u> as many ways as you can think of that plastics can be <u>useful</u> and <u>harmful</u>.

Useful:	Harmful:

"I understand that all settlements need resources, but that overusing some resources can cause harm."

Biome Summary

Look back at Section Three of the Study Book to remind yourself about biomes.

1. Which of these <u>biomes</u> would you prefer to live in? <u>Explain</u> your answer.

I would prefer to live in a...

Woodland biome ☐ *Alpine biome* ☐ *Fresh water biome* ☐

Rainforest biome ☐ *Desert biome* ☐ *Salt water biome* ☐

I would want to live there because ....

....

....

2. In your opinion, which biome is most <u>under threat</u> from humans? How do you think this could be changed?

I think the .... *biome is most under threat.*

This could be changed by ....

....

3. Which <u>biome</u> do you think this picture shows? <u>Explain</u> your answer.

I think this is a .... *biome,*

because ....

....

....

....

4. Colour in the locations of the different biomes around the world
    and create a key to show which colour represents which biome.

Look at the biome map on the inside back cover of the Study Book if you need help.

KEY

"I can name and locate the main biomes of the world and explain how they are different from one another."

Section Four – Climate Change

Climate Change

Pages 30 and 31 in the Study Book take a look at how humans are causing climate change by creating greenhouse gases.

1. Read page 30 of the Study Book. Circle the number below that shows the <u>average temperature</u> of the Earth.

18 °C   –18 °C

15 °C   28 °C   –15 °C

2. Draw a <u>diagram</u> of the Earth to show how the <u>greenhouse effect</u> is caused.

3. In your own words, explain what '<u>climate change</u>' means.

....

....

....

4. One reason for the increasing amount of <u>greenhouse gases</u> in the atmosphere is that the <u>population</u> of the Earth is <u>growing</u>. The graph below shows the size of the Earth's <u>population</u> from 1750 until 2010. Use the graph to help you complete the sentences.

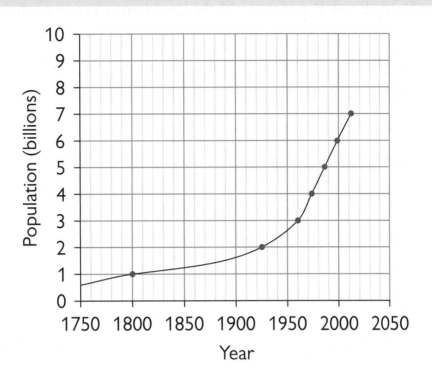

In 1800 the population of Earth was ....

It took .... *years for the population to double from the number it had been in 1800.*

In the year 2000, the population was about ....

5. Why has an increase in the number of people using <u>cars</u> caused the amount of <u>greenhouse gases</u> in our atmosphere to <u>increase</u>?

....

....

....

"I know how human actions are causing an increase in greenhouse gases and why this causes climate change."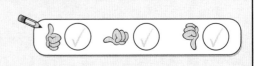

Effects of Climate Change

Climate change can have lots of different effects on people and wildlife. Pages 32 and 33 of the Study Book show some of the problems climate change can cause.

1. Look at the effects of climate change on pages 32 and 33 of the Study Book. Design a T-shirt to warn people about one of these effects.

2. The oceans absorb greenhouse gases, which changes the water and can harm ocean creatures. Why could this be a problem for humans?

....

....

....

3. Look at the effects of <u>climate change</u> on pages 32 and 33 of the Study Book. <u>Sort</u> the effects that are listed below into the grid to show what they could affect. Some might fit into more than one group.

| Wildfires | Extreme weather | Melting ice |

| Carbon dioxide rising in the ocean | Droughts | Sea level rising |

Health	Homes
Farming	**Wildlife**

4. Look at the effects of <u>climate change</u> on pages 32 and 33 of the Study Book. Which one do you think is the <u>biggest problem</u>? Explain your answer.

The biggest problem is ....

because ....

....

....

....

"I know the effects that climate change can have and why these can cause problems for people and wildlife."

The Future

Pages 34 and 35 of the Study Book show some of the ways that we can reduce the amount of greenhouse gases we produce, so that we can try to stop climate change.

1. Can you find the 13 words related to climate change in the word search below? Circle the words and cross them off the list as you find them.

reuse

reduce

greenhouse

oil

coal

global

warming

gases

recycle

environment

fossil fuels

atmosphere

carbon dioxide

J	C	O	A	L	K	Q	B	R	S	B	Y	O	B	X
N	T	C	A	R	B	O	N	D	I	O	X	I	D	E
C	H	F	A	U	B	L	G	L	O	B	A	L	L	F
L	E	O	C	Y	C	E	R	K	L	X	C	P	C	Y
A	E	S	R	N	S	I	R	P	M	B	Y	L	T	D
T	G	S	C	E	B	K	O	L	J	M	O	B	P	E
M	Y	I	E	N	V	I	R	O	N	M	E	N	T	G
O	C	L	H	B	X	K	H	C	K	B	F	I	F	G
S	W	F	E	P	N	B	R	R	N	D	E	X	Z	R
P	A	U	R	S	G	R	E	E	N	H	O	U	S	E
H	R	E	C	Y	C	L	E	U	H	G	I	X	T	D
E	M	L	G	G	R	E	H	S	Q	W	Z	I	F	U
R	I	S	Z	L	T	N	R	E	S	U	Y	F	D	C
E	N	S	Y	C	E	G	N	Z	N	I	P	R	A	E
E	G	U	A	N	Q	J	G	A	S	E	S	Q	X	V

2. List as many different types of renewable energy as you can. Some are mentioned on page 34 of the Study Book.

3. Page 35 of the Study Book shows some ways we can <u>reduce global warming</u>.
<u>How</u> do each of the actions below help to reduce global warming?

Recycling a plastic cup helps because ....

....

....

Switching off lights when they're not needed helps because ....

....

....

4. A primary school class is planning a <u>class picnic</u> in their local park. The <u>plan</u>
they have written is shown below. Write down <u>three</u> ways that they could
change their plan to reduce the <u>impact</u> of their picnic on the <u>environment</u>.

<table>
<tr><td>

<u>Class 5B's Picnic Plan</u>

- Send a letter to each pupil's family with details of the picnic.
- Ask everyone to bring enough food for themselves.
- The school will provide one paper plate and one plastic bottle of water for each pupil.
- The school minibus will take us to the park.
- After the picnic we should collect up and throw away the used plates and bottles.

</td><td>

1) ....

....

....

2) ....

....

....

3) ....

....

....

</td></tr>
</table>

"I know how renewable energy and reducing greenhouse gases can help stop climate change."

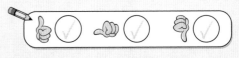

Acknowledgements

p16 © iStock.com/FrankRamspott

Thumb illustration used throughout the book © iStock.com

GLW21